WORKBOOK

Church

Inside

Out

by

Timothy Archer

D1362092

ISBN: 978-0-89098-916-6

©2016 by 21st Century Christian

2809 12th Ave S, Nashville, TN 37204

All rights reserved.

Unless otherwise noted Scripture quotations are from the New International Version.

Scripture quotations taken from THE HOLY BIBLE, NEW INTERNATIONAL VERSION®, NIV®

Copyright © 1973, 1978, 1984, 2011 by Biblica, Inc.™

Used by permission. All rights reserved worldwide.

Cover design by Jonathan Edelhuber

TABLE OF CONTENTS

CHAPTER 1
Church Inside Out **5**

CHAPTER 2
The Inward-Focused Church **11**

CHAPTER 3
Members Only **17**

CHAPTER 4
Accentuating the Negative **23**

CHAPTER 5
Diplomatic Mission **31**

CHAPTER 6
Who Is My Neighbor? **39**

CHAPTER 7
Eating with Sinners **47**

CHAPTER 8
A Life Like Lightning **53**

CHAPTER 9
Preparing for Harvest **59**

CHAPTER 10
A Son of Shalom **65**

CHAPTER 11
Good News Is for Sharing **71**

CHAPTER 12
Citizens of the Kingdom **77**

CHAPTER 13
Being the Church, Inside and Out **85**

CHAPTER 1

CHURCH INSIDE OUT

Welcome to the study guide for *Church Inside Out*. This study guide contains thought questions about the ideas presented in the book, additional observations and commentary, and a proposed group study plan.

As we begin

As we begin this study, what do you hope to take away that you can use in your own life?

What do you hope to take away that you can use in your congregation?

Cultural shifts

Throughout the Bible, we see evidence of cultural shifts and changing religious attitudes. There were times when it was easy to be a follower of God; there were times when it was extremely difficult.

Foreign nations often dominated the Israelites and their land. These nations frequently made fun of the God of Israel and His inability to protect His people. Those times tended to turn people back to God. It was the times of prosperity that would lead God's people to seek other gods, to want to imitate the peoples around them and join them in their worship.

Consider these examples:

> Then a new king, to whom Joseph meant nothing, came to power in Egypt. "Look," he said to his people, "the Israelites have become far too numerous for us. Come, we must deal shrewdly with them or they will become even more numerous and, if war breaks out, will join our enemies, fight against us and leave the country" (Exodus 1:8–10).

Joseph had risen to a position of power and authority in Egypt. He settled his family there, in an area where they could live quietly and worship God as they chose. But after his death, a new king came along who only knew that these foreigners were living in his land. God's people entered into a long period of oppression at the hands of the Egyptians.

> After that whole generation had been gathered to their ancestors, another generation grew up who knew neither the LORD nor what he had done for Israel. Then the Israelites did evil in the eyes of the LORD and served the Baals. They forsook the LORD, the God of their fathers, who had brought them out of Egypt (Judges 2:10–12).

Throughout the book of Judges, God's people run hot and cold. They forget God and begin worshiping other gods. God sends a foreign army to oppress them. They cry out to God, and God sends a deliverer. While the deliverer is alive, the people serve God. Once this hero dies, the people turn away from God, and the cycle starts over.

> Then a voice said to him, "What are you doing here, Elijah?" He replied, "I have been very zealous for the LORD God Almighty. The Israelites have rejected your covenant, torn down your altars, and put your prophets to death with the sword. I am the only one left, and now they are trying to kill me too" (1 Kings 19:13–14).

Elijah lived in the time of King Ahab and his foreign wife, Queen Jezebel. Not only did Jezebel impose the religion of her people on the nation of Israel, but she also persecuted those who continued to worship God. Elijah was one of the few who were able to stand up to her, but he thought he was the only one. (God would let him know that there were still seven thousand others who remained faithful.)

Josiah removed all the detestable idols from all the territory belonging to the Israelites, and he had all who were present in Israel serve the LORD their God. As long as he lived, they did not fail to follow the LORD, the God of their ancestors (2 Chronicles 34:33).

Sometimes cultural shifts are for the good in the Bible. Here we see that Josiah led a religious reform that brought the nation of Israel back to God. He restored the temple, got rid of idols and pagan priests, and led the people to pledge themselves to fulfill the Law.

On that day a great persecution broke out against the church in Jerusalem, and all except the apostles were scattered throughout Judea and Samaria. Godly men buried Stephen and mourned deeply for him. But Saul began to destroy the church. Going from house to house, he dragged off men and women and put them in prison (Acts 8:1–3).

After the murder of Stephen, a strong time of persecution came against the church. Christians were arrested, and entire churches were threatened. Of course, God would later take care of the leader of this persecution, turning Saul into the Apostle Paul, one of the great champions of faith in the early church.

During all of these times of cultural change, God was still at work. Some of his greatest miracles happened during the time of Moses and that of Elijah. The time of persecution in the book of Acts allowed the church to expand beyond Jerusalem and Judea. The period of captivity strengthened the nation of Israel. The rise of the Roman Empire created the right conditions for the coming of the Messiah and the birth of the church.

God is at work today. Even as Christianity seems to be in decline in the U.S, God is doing great things through His church. We can choose to be a part of it or choose to peer out through the windows of our church building as others spread the kingdom.

How has the church's role in society changed during your lifetime? What have you been able to observe?

Do you feel that society is more or less friendly to Christianity? Why do you feel that way?

What changes have you noticed in your community regarding religion?

Are there other major changes that have affected your church? (population growth or decline in your area, changes in makeup of population, new city ordinances, youth sports activities)

Look at the following list of challenges facing the church. Which do you see as being the most critical? (Rank them from 1 to 8)

_____ Lack of interest in the church among younger generations

_____ Doctrinal changes within the church

_____ Hostile attitude of society toward Christianity

_____ Rise of Islam and other religions

_____ General apathy among church members

_____ Pressures of life in our modern society

_____ Church members' lack of biblical knowledge

_____ "Majoring in the minors"; church's misplaced focus

What other challenges would you include?

Annual physical

As we begin discussing your congregation and its outreach to the surrounding community, let's try to take some vital signs. Put an X in the box that best describes where you consider your church to be.

MEMBERSHIP

Declining		About the same		Growing

ATTENDANCE

Declining		About the same		Growing

AVERAGE AGE OF THE CONGREGATION

Younger		About the same		Older

LEVEL OF INVOLVEMENT OF MEMBERS

Declining		About the same		Growing

OUTREACH

Declining	About the same			Growing

VISIBILITY IN THE COMMUNITY

Declining	About the same			Growing

INFLUENCE IN THE COMMUNITY

Declining	About the same			Growing

Remember that this is merely a description of how things are. It isn't a reflection of what the church would like to be or what it's going to be in the future.

When you go to the doctor, you see things as they are. You may want to weigh less and plan to lose weight; the numbers on the scale merely reflect where you are right now.

If you could miraculously improve one of the above areas, which one would you improve?

In which area(s) do you feel your church is already doing as well as it can?

Which of the areas do you feel will get worse if left unattended? Which areas will improve naturally if things stay as they are?

Before moving on, spend some time praying about your congregation's current situation and prospects for the future.

CHAPTER 2

THE INWARD-FOCUSED CHURCH

When God called Jonah to go preach to Nineveh, Jonah didn't want to go. It wasn't that he was afraid of the Assyrians. It was because he was afraid that God would forgive the Assyrians if they repented! He didn't want his enemies to be spared. Jonah had to be reminded that God also cared about the 120 thousand people in that city, even if they weren't Jews (Jonah 4:11).

God told Isaiah:

> It is too small a thing for you to be my servant to restore the tribes of Jacob and bring back those of Israel I have kept. I will also make you a light for the Gentiles, that my salvation may reach to the ends of the earth (Isaiah 49:6).

God's plan was that his people would share the message with everyone around, not just the Jews.

Understanding the reach of God's love was one of the challenges of the early church. Although Peter had preached on the day of Pentecost that the promise was for all, it took years for the early Christians to realize that "all" included non-Jews.

The church similarly wrestles with grasping the fact that it isn't enough just to minister to those within the walls of our church building; we have to turn our focus outward.

Vision check

Let's go through some questions to help you analyze where the focus of your church lies. We'll look at the seven traits of inward-focused churches, then analyze how your congregation is doing with each. (Mark one of the boxes under each statement in the chart)

1. Inward-focused churches fight among themselves.

Our church is able to work together without arguing or complaining.				
Never	Rarely	Sometimes	Often	Always

People are more focused on preserving the church as is than they are on reaching out.				
Never	Rarely	Sometimes	Often	Always

People in our church talk about "us" and "them" when discussing other members.				
Never	Rarely	Sometimes	Often	Always

We are more focused on doing what needs to be done than we are on getting our own way.				
Never	Rarely	Sometimes	Often	Always

2. Inward-focused churches look backward, not forward.

People in our church talk more about the past than about plans for the future.				
Never	Rarely	Sometimes	Often	Always

Our church is willing to try things we've never done before.				
Never	Rarely	Sometimes	Often	Always

Our church is willing to consider doing things that didn't work in the past.				
Never	Rarely	Sometimes	Often	Always

We have trouble appreciating what is happening today because we compare it with the past.				
Never	Rarely	Sometimes	Often	Always

3. Inward-focused churches have lots of meetings.

Our church limits meetings to the ones that are truly necessary.				
Never	Rarely	Sometimes	Often	Always
We spend more time talking about ministry than actually doing ministry.				
Never	Rarely	Sometimes	Often	Always
Our meetings focus on problems with church members, church staff, and church facilities.				
Never	Rarely	Sometimes	Often	Always
Meetings in our church are times of empowering and guiding members in their ministries.				
Never	Rarely	Sometimes	Often	Always

4. Inward-focused churches use their resources for themselves.

Our church budget is used primarily for the benefit of the members of our congregation.				
Never	Rarely	Sometimes	Often	Always
We use our funds more for long-term mission projects than short-term trips by our members.				
Never	Rarely	Sometimes	Often	Always
We see our building as a tool for ministry and outreach.				
Never	Rarely	Sometimes	Often	Always
Our staff is expected to dedicate more time to serving the church than reaching out to others.				
Never	Rarely	Sometimes	Often	Always

5. Inward-focused churches have members that put their own needs first.

Our members focus more on ministering to others rather than being ministered to.				
Never	Rarely	Sometimes	Often	Always
Longtime members and big givers expect to have great influence in the congregation.				
Never	Rarely	Sometimes	Often	Always
In our church, we hear complaints from members who say they aren't being fed.				
Never	Rarely	Sometimes	Often	Always
Our members expect and demand visits from the staff on a regular basis.				
Never	Rarely	Sometimes	Often	Always

6. Inward-focused churches resist change.

Members of our congregation work together to make changes when necessary.				
Never	Rarely	Sometimes	Often	Always
We expect to always be able to do things the way we are used to doing them.				
Never	Rarely	Sometimes	Often	Always
Our goal is to keep our members satisfied instead of making it easier for outsiders to join us.				
Never	Rarely	Sometimes	Often	Always
We won't change for the sake of change, but we will make adjustments to reach more people.				
Never	Rarely	Sometimes	Often	Always

7. Inward-focused churches celebrate the wrong things.

Only people who lead in public worship receive praise and recognition in our church.				
Never	Rarely	Sometimes	Often	Always
We look for opportunities to spotlight ministries that typically go unnoticed.				
Never	Rarely	Sometimes	Often	Always
We keep an outward focus when talking about the ministries of our church.				
Never	Rarely	Sometimes	Often	Always
When talking with outsiders, we talk more about the church than we do about Christ.				
Never	Rarely	Sometimes	Often	Always

Looking at your answers, which areas do you think the church should focus on to improve its outward focus?

Do you disagree with any of the traits that were mentioned? Why or why not?

Survival instinct

Human organizations have a tendency to make their continuing existence a high priority, if not the highest. That makes sense for some groups, but not for the local church. We know that we are part of a greater body that will never cease to exist. We don't have to worry about whether or not the current manifestation of the Lord's church continues to function; the church will never cease to be.

In what ways can a congregation concern itself more with survival than with ministry?

Is there ever a time when it's better for a congregation to close its doors? When might that be the best option?

How do we maintain the balance between mission and sustainability? That is, how do we step out in faith as a church without being irresponsible?

Timing

Can you think of stages in a church's life when an inward focus is appropriate?

How can a congregation know when it's time to focus more on building the kingdom than merely fortifying itself?

CHAPTER 3

MEMBERS ONLY

Let's go on a field trip. If you can't go there physically, try to picture your church's building in your mind. Now complete these statements with the best responses, as if you were a first-time visitor:

As I look for the building, I find that

____ it's almost impossible to find

____ it's difficult to know where to turn

____ The building is easy to locate

____ (other)_____

_____

When I go to park,

____ there is clear, convenient visitor parking

____ someone helps me find a place

____ I'm not sure where to park

____ (other)_____

_____

As I approach the building,

____ the best entrance for me is clearly marked

____ someone opens the door and welcomes me

____ I'm not sure which door to use

____ (other)_____

_____

In the foyer,

____ The foyer? What's a foyer?

____ it's full of people, making it hard to walk

____ people are waiting to help me find my way

____ (other)_____

_____

Another interesting exercise is to ask someone to come as a "mystery visitor." Or you can just interview some new members, asking them to think back to their first visit to your building. You might be surprised to hear their insights.

What changes could be made to improve your visitors' first impressions of your building?

When you meet together

Now let's talk about what most visitors will see as the focal point: the assembly. Would you say...

Announcements are limited to what is strictly necessary	Yes	No
Pew bulletins give information outsiders can understand	Yes	No
Explanations are given about each part of worship	Yes	No
We avoid putting visitors on the spot during greeting times	Yes	No

Church members are aware of visitors and help them, as necessary	Yes	No
All slides used are attractive and easy to read	Yes	No
Song lyrics are readily available to visitors (through books or slides)	Yes	No
Visitors know what is expected of them during the Lord's Supper	Yes	No
Sermons aren't usually aimed at visitors	Yes	No
Sermons are intelligible to outsiders	Yes	No

We can make our assemblies times of worshiping God and encouraging one another while still providing a positive experience for visitors.

What changes could be made to improve your visitors' experience in the assembly?

An Outsider's Guide to the Lord's Supper

From a visitor's point of view, the Lord's Supper is one of the most stressful and potentially baffling parts of the assembly. They're likely to be uncertain about what things mean, what they are supposed to do, and what they aren't supposed to do.

To be honest, this can even be tricky for Christians visiting another congregation. Some churches stand for the Lord's Supper. Some hold the elements until everyone has been served. Some pass the tray of cups twice, once for people to take their cup, the second time for putting it back.

Here's an exercise in thinking about things from an outsider's viewpoint. Think about the sorts of things you would put in a "user's manual" for the Lord's Supper at your church. What would you write about the following areas?

What is the Lord's Supper? (What does it mean? What does it symbolize?)

Who takes the Lord's Supper? (Members only? Adults only? Any baptized believer? Everyone in attendance? Do you take it more than once on a Sunday?)

What are the mechanics of taking the bread? (Do you break off a piece? Do you take what's already broken? How much should you take?)

What are the mechanics of taking the cup? (Do you put your cup back? Do you put it in a special row on the plate? Do you leave it in the back of your pew? Will the tray be passed again to collect the cup?)

Does your congregation do anything that might be out of the ordinary? Any other suggestions for an outsider?

Watch your language!

It's easy to forget that many terms that seem so natural to us can be foreign to an outsider. We talk about "the Supper," knowing that it isn't as much a supper as a symbolic time of eating and drinking. There are many such words and phrases we may need to explain to our visitors.

It's interesting to note how often the gospel writers explained the meaning of a place name or a term they used. They didn't take it for granted that their readers knew those things; they made the meaning clear. That's something that our churches need to do as well.

We should also remember that the New Testament was written in *Koiné* Greek, the common language of the street, not the Classical Greek used by the highly educated. Communication was the goal.

Try your hand at improving Sunday assembly communication. Here are some things you might hear in a church assembly. How could you better phrase them so that outsiders would know what you are talking about?

"Separate and apart from communion, we now follow the command to lay by in store on the first day of the week. Each should give as he has purposed in his heart, according to how the Lord has prospered him."

"If anyone today wants to respond to the gospel and put on their Lord in baptism or feels the need to repent and be restored to the church, come forward as we stand and sing."

"We will have a Brother's Keepers fellowship today following this morning's assembly. The elders and their wives will be hosting. All visitors are welcome to join us."

It would get extremely tedious to explain every term every Sunday. We wouldn't want to give a full explanation of the Lord's Supper week in and week out. We can't explain who deacons and elders are every time we mention them.

How do we find a balance between making worship language acceptable to outsiders yet not turning every service into a Christian vocabulary lesson?

How do we balance the need to edify church members with the need to make outsiders feel welcome?

Lastly, how do we meet the needs of Christians and non-Christians in our assemblies while still focusing on worshiping and glorifying God?

CHAPTER 4

ACCENTUATING
THE NEGATIVE

In this chapter, we talk about the yeast of the Pharisees. What are some of the things that we see about the Pharisees in the gospels?

1. They focused on details, rather than the principles behind the Law:

   "Woe to you, teachers of the law and Pharisees, you hypocrites! You give a tenth of your spices—mint, dill and cumin. But you have neglected the more important matters of the law—justice, mercy and faithfulness. You should have practiced the latter, without neglecting the former." (Matthew 23:23)

2. They focused on the external aspects of religion, rather than the internal:

   "Woe to you, teachers of the law and Pharisees, you hypocrites! You clean the outside of the cup and dish, but inside they are full of greed and self-indulgence. Blind Pharisee! First clean the inside of the cup and dish, and then the outside also will be clean. "Woe to you, teachers of the law and Pharisees, you hypocrites! You are like whitewashed tombs, which look beautiful on the outside but on the inside are full of the bones of the dead and everything unclean" (Matthew 23:25–27).

3. They put much emphasis on their traditions:

   The Pharisees and all the Jews do not eat unless they give their hands a ceremonial washing, holding to the tradition of the elders. When they come from the marketplace they do not eat unless they wash. And they observe many other traditions, such as the washing of cups, pitchers and kettles. (Mark 7:3–4)

4. They considered themselves superior to other believers:

"You mean he has deceived you also?" the Pharisees retorted. "Have any of the rulers or of the Pharisees believed in him? No! But this mob that knows nothing of the law—there is a curse on them" (John 7:47–49).

5. They refused to have contact with people they considered to be sinners:

But the Pharisees and the teachers of the law muttered, "This man welcomes sinners and eats with them" (Luke 15:2).

When the Pharisee who had invited him saw this, he said to himself, "If this man were a prophet, he would know who is touching him and what kind of woman she is—that she is a sinner" (Luke 7:39).

6. They kicked out anyone who dared follow someone with whom they disagreed:

His parents said this because they were afraid of the Jewish leaders, who already had decided that anyone who acknowledged that Jesus was the Messiah would be put out of the synagogue (John 9:22).

Yet at the same time many even among the leaders believed in him. But because of the Pharisees they would not openly acknowledge their faith for fear they would be put out of the synagogue (John 12:42).

Yet we do well to remember that the Pharisees weren't always that way. Historically, they were devout people who were trying to follow God. It's interesting to note that Paul never criticizes the Pharisees; he doesn't hesitate to identify himself as being one!

Why do you think many of the Pharisees of Jesus' day became legalistic, judgmental hypocrites?

How can Christians today avoid falling into that trap?

Unleavened Church

Let's look at the signs that a church has been influenced by Pharisee-like teaching, trying to see if our congregation has been infected.

1. Instead of being known for love, they are known for judgment.

Outsiders view our church as a loving group				
Never	Rarely	Sometimes	Often	Always
Outsiders view our church as a judgmental group.				
Never	Rarely	Sometimes	Often	Always
Our focus on sound doctrine leads us to love and accept one another.				
Never	Rarely	Sometimes	Often	Always
Our focus on sound doctrine leads us to criticize and question one another.				
Never	Rarely	Sometimes	Often	Always
When we talk about other churches, our love for them is obvious.				
Never	Rarely	Sometimes	Often	Always
When we talk about other churches, we focus on their shortcomings.				
Never	Rarely	Sometimes	Often	Always

2. These churches specialize in pointing out the sins of others.

We publicly denounce the sins of people who aren't members of our church.				
Never	Rarely	Sometimes	Often	Always
We publicly recognize our sin, knowing that we are no better than others.				
Never	Rarely	Sometimes	Often	Always
When we talk about those practicing sin, we do so with anger and disdain.				
Never	Rarely	Sometimes	Often	Always
When we talk about those practicing sin, we do so with sadness and hope for repentance.				
Never	Rarely	Sometimes	Often	Always
The world hears the message: "You are a sinner; we are holy."				
Never	Rarely	Sometimes	Often	Always
The world hears the message: "We are all sinners in need of God's grace."				
Never	Rarely	Sometimes	Often	Always

3. They are much better at telling you what they aren't than what they are.

People outside the church define us by what we believe and for the values for which we stand.				
Never	Rarely	Sometimes	Often	Always
People outside the church define us by the things we're against.				
Never	Rarely	Sometimes	Often	Always
We see ourselves as working with the community to produce good works.				
Never	Rarely	Sometimes	Often	Always
We see ourselves as opposing the community, working to make it more like us.				
Never	Rarely	Sometimes	Often	Always

4. They emphasize "avoiding the appearance of evil."

We sometimes avoid certain people because of what others might think.				
Never	Rarely	Sometimes	Often	Always
We are willing to spend time and share meals with anyone.				
Never	Rarely	Sometimes	Often	Always
Knowing that "bad company corrupts good morals," we spend our time with people who think like us.				
Never	Rarely	Sometimes	Often	Always
We do our best to follow Jesus' example of being with the people who most need to hear the good news.				
Never	Rarely	Sometimes	Often	Always

5. More is said about withdrawing from others than drawing near to God.

We believe that Christians can live in unity even when they don't agree on everything.				
Never	Rarely	Sometimes	Often	Always
We insist that everyone believe as we do if they want to call themselves our brothers.				
Never	Rarely	Sometimes	Often	Always
We are willing to spend time with everyone, even those who differ from us religiously.				
Never	Rarely	Sometimes	Often	Always
We not only avoid certain Christians, we also avoid those who fellowship them.				
Never	Rarely	Sometimes	Often	Always
We focus on drawing near to God, letting Him be the judge of our fellow men.				
Never	Rarely	Sometimes	Often	Always
We draw near to God by avoiding those that teach things we can't accept.				
Never	Rarely	Sometimes	Often	Always

6. People around them hear a message of condemnation rather than a message of good news.

The world hears condemnation when we speak to them of the Bible.				
Never	Rarely	Sometimes	Often	Always
The world hears good news when we speak to them of the Bible.				
Never	Rarely	Sometimes	Often	Always
We come across as judgmental when we speak of our beliefs.				
Never	Rarely	Sometimes	Often	Always
We project an air of humility when we speak of our beliefs.				
Never	Rarely	Sometimes	Often	Always

The worldly church

Jesus also warned His disciples against two other "yeasts": that of the Sadducees and that of Herod. Both of these have to do with conforming to the ways of this world.

In the book, we talked about the Sadducees, how they were a pragmatic group that adapted to the culture to gain power. As long as the Sadducees maintained their status and their power, they were willing to let outsiders tell them what to do.

Herod was an Idumean who came to rule over what is now Palestine. He and his family used religion as a means to obtain political power. They were not faithful Jews, but manipulated Jewish faith for their own ends. Herod I named high priests from his wife's family, seizing control of the leadership of the Jews. He built the great temple in Jerusalem not out of a desire to worship, but as a means to solidify his political standing.

The yeast of Herod is the allure of politics, the quest for power. When religious movements join forces with political groups, the political groups are strengthened and the religious movements are weakened.

Let's ask some questions to see if your church may be suffering from the effects of the yeast of the Sadducees and of Herod.

Does your church blend in with its environment?	Yes	No

We want to be able to communicate with our culture in ways that non-believers can understand. We don't want to become just like those non-believers. It's crucial that Christians maintain distance between themselves and the world's influences.

Do your beliefs change as culture changes?	Yes	No

We can change the way we talk about our beliefs. We can change the way we do certain things based on our beliefs. But our core beliefs can't be subject to the whims of culture.

Does your outreach look like that done by secular groups?	Yes	No

Too many churches have ceased to include Jesus in their dealings with their community. They build houses, offer food, provide clothes, but say nothing about the lordship of Jesus and the salvation He offers. Aid should never be predicated on the acceptance of the gospel, but if we help people without offering them the hope of salvation, we haven't really helped them at all.

Have you made a certain political stance a key component of your identity?	Yes	No

Jesus was willing to call both the tax collector Matthew (who worked for the government) and the zealot Simon (who longed to see the government overthrown).

If people perceive us as being on one side or the other in the political world, they'll be less likely to listen to what we have to say. Our message will be heard as mere partisan propaganda.

Christians have a duty to speak out against evil in this world. There is no reason for us to remain silent on the issues that affect society. But we will always have a stronger message when we speak from outside the system than from inside. There's a reason why sports officials don't wear the team colors of either team during a game; if you are part of the contest, you lose your objectivity.

Are members more interested in the political state of the country than the salvation of those around them?	Yes	No

Too often Christians see politics as the only means to impact society. In this mindset, evil can only be controlled through legislation and legislation can only be enacted by politicians, so the church must align itself with some candidate or some political party. That's the yeast of Herod!

The church has a mission to change society...through the gospel of Jesus Christ. When we say the only way to change the world is through politics, we deny the power of the gospel. We doubt the ability of God to work in His world. We put our faith in humans rather than God Himself.

CHAPTER 5

DIPLOMATIC MISSION

The longest prayer of Jesus that we have recorded in the Bible is found in John 17. In this prayer, Jesus has much to say about the world.

Some of what He says is about the physical world, the planet on which we live (John 17:5, 24). Most of the references, however, have to do with the unbelieving world, that segment of society that doesn't follow God.

Jesus tells us the following about the world in John 17:

▶ The disciples were called out of the world (17:6).

▶ Even so, they are still in the world, just not of the world (17:11, 14-16).

▶ The world does not know God (17:25).

▶ The world hates believers because they are not of the world (17:14).

▶ The disciples have been sent into the world (17:18).

▶ Believers must be united that the world may know (17:23) and believe (17:21) that God has sent them.

All of this is still true. The Christian community lives as foreigners in a hostile world, a world that is not our home. Yet we have a mission here, having been sent to help people know God and believe in Him.

Citizens

The people of Philippi were proud of their Roman citizenship. In Acts, when first mentioning Philippi, Luke writes: "From there we traveled to Philippi, a Roman colony and the leading city of that district of Macedonia" (Acts 16:12). Octavian had granted Philippi colonial status after his war with Anthony. As a colony, everything in Philippi was set up just like Rome. Roman citizens in Philippi had all the rights and privileges of a Roman in Rome itself.

Many ex-soldiers settled in Philippi. The city was considered Italian soil. Citizens of Philippi were automatically Roman citizens as well. Rome considered Philippi to be a model of Roman culture for the surrounding area, an example of what a good Roman city should be and its citizens were expected to live as model Roman citizens.

The apostle Paul makes use of this civic pride to call them to another loyalty. In verse 27 of chapter 1, Paul uses the Greek word politeuomai, which literally means to live as a citizen. Most English versions obscure the literal meaning, but a few try to capture Paul's imagery in Philippians 1:27:

> "Live as citizens who reflect the Good News about Christ." (God's Word)

> "Above all, you must live as citizens of heaven, conducting yourselves in a manner worthy of the Good News about Christ." (New Living Translation)

> "Whatever happens, as citizens of heaven live in a manner worthy of the gospel of Christ." (Today's New International Version)

How do Christians show through their lives that they are citizens of heaven and not citizens of this world?

Strangers in a strange land

There are different kinds of foreigners. Think about the following categories:

tourists   immigrants   refugees   pilgrims

What's the difference between these categories? What is each looking to do while in their host country? Which of these plan to make a home in their host country?

Now think about ambassadors. How is the role of ambassador different from the four categories above?

If we apply the above categories to churches, we find the following:

The tourist church:

Focused on enjoyment. Interested in observing community around, but only out of a sense of curiosity. Caught up in own programs, aiming to keep everyone happy.

No desire to learn to relate to community around. Goal is to have a good time then go home.

The immigrant church:

Goal is to become part of the community. Downplays unique Christian beliefs and values; emphasizes things that resonate with those around.

Eager to change and fit in. Goal is to make a home and live in it as long as possible.

The refugee church:

Forced to live in this world, like it or not. Hiding from the hostile society outside, this church focuses on itself and resists all attempts to make it change.

Powerless by choice, not influencing society at all. Goal is to survive time on earth.

The pilgrim church:

Definitely "just a passin' through." No time for worldly concerns, this church lives with its head in the clouds. Life is all about worship and holiness; anything else is beneath the consideration of these Christians. Goal is to pass through this world thinking only of heaven.

The ambassador church:

This church is here to share God's kingdom with others. This is done through words, but also through a lifestyle.

This church studies the culture that surrounds it, not to imitate it, but to be able to communicate God's message in an understandable way. The goal is to faithfully represent God's interests in this world, inviting others to be a part of the mission.

What does this look like in real life? Let's look at a few scenarios. Read the situation, then look at the different church reactions. Offer your suggestion as to how an ambassador church might respond.

Scenario 1:

In December, your church is offered a chance to provide gifts for children at a local elementary school.

- **Tourist Church:** "Sounds like fun! Can we get the newspaper to come take pictures? Maybe we can make the front page."
- **Immigrant Church:** "We'll happily provide gifts. And we'll be careful to avoid any reference to Christmas or other things that might be considered religious. Just gifts with Season's Greetings tags."
- **Refugee Church:** "We can't participate in anything that might sound like we're celebrating a pagan holiday. Thanks, but no thanks."
- **Pilgrim Church:** "We can give the children New Testaments and Bible reading plans for the new year."
- **Ambassador Church:**

Scenario 2:

Heavy rains have hit your town. Poorer sections of town are flooded and have been evacuated.

- **Tourist Church:** "Sure glad the water didn't get up to our building! Hope the roads clear in time for movie night tomorrow night."
- **Immigrant Church:** "We're taking up a collection to give to the Community Chest. Our members really get behind projects like this."
- **Refugee Church:** "Our offering is for the saints, not for the world. We'll help any of our members who were affected by this disaster."
- **Pilgrim Church:** "We're going to have a twenty-four hour prayer vigil on behalf of those affected."
- **Ambassador Church:**

Scenario 3:

There is a gay pride parade scheduled for Saturday, with the route passing right in front of your building. Saturday is also when you have a church-wide event in your building.

- **Tourist Church:** "We'll take a break and watch the parade, then get back to our fun."
- **Immigrant Church:** "We'll dismiss our event and join the parade. We want to show our solidarity."
- **Refugee Church:** "We'll postpone our event, just to make sure that nobody confuses us with them. We must avoid all appearances of evil!"
- **Pilgrim Church:** "The parade really shouldn't affect us. We'll be inside, worshiping as planned."
- **Ambassador Church:**

Manning the embassy

Let's look again at the skills of a good ambassador, noting how well your church is doing in each of these areas:

1. A good ambassador knows the language and culture of the nation where he serves.

	Yes	No
Our church knows our community well.	Yes	No
We work at communicating the gospel in understandable ways.	Yes	No
We don't change our message, but we do change how we present it.	Yes	No

2. A good ambassador communicates his nation's policies to the people where he serves.

	Yes	No
Our church members know the Bible well.	Yes	No
We are careful to differentiate between our opinions and God's Word.	Yes	No

We try to explain Bible truths in an understandable way.	Yes	No

3. A good ambassador puts his nation's interests ahead of the nation where he serves.

We are Christians first, citizens of this country second.	Yes	No
We put God's kingdom ahead of our own prosperity.	Yes	No
We emphasize God's values, not those of our country.	Yes	No

4. A good ambassador knows how to advise those wanting to become a part of his nation.

We actively seek to identify those wanting to know God better.	Yes	No
We can present our beliefs to those who ask us.	Yes	No
When our members don't know how to respond to someone's questions, they know to whom they should go. There is always someone who can teach them the gospel.	Yes	No

Sure of who we are

I grew up hearing people say that the Bible teaches us to be good citizens. As I've studied the Bible over the years, I've found that's not exactly true. More than good citizens, the Bible calls us to be good foreigners.

During my years in Argentina, I obeyed the laws. I paid taxes. I honored and respected leaders. All of these are things Christians are told to do. But I didn't have to become Argentine to do those things. Those are all things that foreigners can do. You don't have to be a good citizen to be a good community member. You can be a good foreigner.

In Philippians 3:19-20, Paul contrasts being a citizen of heaven with having your mind on earthly things. The Philippians were proud of their Roman citizenship, but Paul tells them they need to be proud of their heavenly citizenship. They are citizens of heaven and need to recognize that. To fail to do that is to have your mind on earthly things.

John 13 says that Jesus could serve others because He knew He came from God and was returning to God. The same holds true for our churches. If we know who we are, we can fulfill our mission.

Why do we need an awareness of having come from God? How does that help us live as God's representatives?

How does knowing that we are returning to God help us better serve the world?

Think back on the parable of the life-saving station. What does that story tell us about how a church can forget its mission?

What can we do to be sure we don't forget our purpose in this world?

CHAPTER 6

WHO IS MY NEIGHBOR?

One of the turning points for the growth of the early church happened when Christians began reaching out to Gentiles as well as Jews. Luke describes that moment this way:

> Now those who had been scattered by the persecution that broke out when Stephen was killed traveled as far as Phoenicia, Cyprus and Antioch, spreading the word only among Jews. Some of them, however, men from Cyprus and Cyrene, went to Antioch and began to speak to Greeks also, telling them the good news about the Lord Jesus. The Lord's hand was with them, and a great number of people believed and turned to the Lord (Acts 11:19–21).

These believers recognized that they were only reaching part of the community. Knowing that the gospel is good news for everyone, they began to speak to those who had been ignored in the past. And God blessed their efforts.

It was out of this context the disciples received a new name:

> Then Barnabas went to Tarsus to look for Saul, and when he found him, he brought him to Antioch. So for a whole year Barnabas and Saul met with the church and taught great numbers of people. The disciples were called Christians first at Antioch (Acts 11:25–26).

Jews and Greeks meeting together. This was something new. What do you call people like that? Christians.

Many of our churches are being called to step across socioeconomic barriers, ethnic barriers, language barriers; they are being called not just to be a black church or a white church or a rich church or a poor church. They are being called to be Christians.

So we look at our communities, learn about them, then find the best ways to minister to our neighbors.

Mapping your neighborhood

On a sheet of paper, draw a map of your neighborhood. (If you live in apartments or other multifamily housing, you may want to draw your building) Living arrangements vary from place to place. For this example, we'll use a fairly standard city block.

Label your own house with an X

		X			

Then label the other houses as best you can.

?	**Gomez**	**?**	**?**	**Karkoffs**	**?**
?	**Johnsons**	**X**	**Ms. Davis**	**Dixons**	**?**

This simple exercise will help you see which of your neighbors you still need to get to know.

How well can you complete the map of your block or building? Did you discover anything by trying to complete this map?

Go back to the map and label the people in each house as: Stranger, Acquaintance, or Friend.

How well do you know your immediate neighbors?

Do you have telephone numbers for the people around you?

What might you do to get to know your neighbors better?

Community analysis

The principle of community analysis is vital for your church. Let's look at a checklist of what needs to be done:

Step 1: Prayer

_____ Commit to pray for neighborhood

_____ Organize prayer walks

_____ Carry out prayer walks in neighborhood around the building

_____ Carry out prayer walks in other target areas in the city

Step 2: Partners

_____ Identify potential partners in the neighborhood (school administrators, business people, non-profit leaders)

_____ Contact potential partners

_____ Interview partners, seeking information about community and recommendations for others who can give insight into community

_____ Interview others who have been identified as potential sources of information

Step 3: Surveys

_____ Prepare survey to be conducted in target neighborhood

_____ Train church members in proper survey techniques

_____ Conduct neighborhood surveys in teams of two

_____ Compile survey results

Step 4: Profiles

_____ Write case studies of typical residents of your area

_____ Prepare recommendations on strategies for ministering in this neighborhood

_____ Make concrete plans as to who, what, when, where, and how to carry out ministry projects

What are some of the things you would hope to learn through this community analysis?

What would be some of the barriers to be overcome in an effort like this?

On the next page, you'll find a sample survey that could be used for community analysis.

Community Needs Survey

Hello, my name is _____ and this is _____.
We're from _____ church. We are conducting a community survey about needs in this area. Would you help us by answering a few questions?

Note respondents gender and approximate age (20-35, 35-50, 50-65, 65+)

How long have you lived in the area?

2 years or less	11-15 years
3-5 years	15+ years
6-10 years	

What two things do you like most about living here?

Job opportunities	Public transportation
Safety	Clean streets and sidewalks
Housing	Park system
Friendly police	Education

What would you say are the two biggest problems in this area?

Safety	Alcohol/drugs
Poverty	Unemployment
Education	No sports programs
Domestic violence	No citizenship classes
Health care	Transportation

Do you think church is an important part of this community?

Why do you think many people don't attend church?

If you were looking for a church in the area, what three things would you look for?

Addiction recovery programs

After-school programs

Anger management classes

Bible classes

Day care

English classes

Help with family and domestic issues

Money management classes

Sports programs

What advice would you give a church that wants to help people in this area?

The best way to tell me about community events is_____

Email

Mail

Newspaper

Posters

Radio

Television

Would you like to give your name and address to receive information in the future?

Name_____

Address_____

Email_____

Thank you for your help!

Coming to America

Is your church open to the idea of a multi-cultural outreach? Why or why not?

What are some of the immigrant groups within your community?

What are some services your church could offer to these people? (English classes, citizenship classes, financial planning, health clinics)

What are some of the minorities within your community that aren't presently being served by your congregation?

How could you reach out to some of these groups and make them feel welcome at your church?

CHAPTER 7

EATING
WITH SINNERS

There are two interesting stories in John 2. In the first, Jesus and His disciples are at a wedding feast in Cana. A typical wedding feast included most of the people in town, if not all. These parties would go on for days, with much eating, drinking, and merry-making. Some would argue that this was no place for a holy man.

Later Jesus goes to the temple in Jerusalem. Seems a more fitting place for the Messiah, right? This was the place where faithful Jews from around the world went to worship God. There would be no wild parties there. Yet it was there that Jesus felt the need to confront the sin that was present.

For most of us, red warning lights would have been flashing in our heads while at the party; those lights would have been turned off when entering the temple grounds. So it's ironic to see that Jesus provides what is needed to let the party continue (where common people enjoyed God's gifts), but He puts a stop to what is happening in the temple (where unholy men were carrying out unholy business).

Throughout Jesus' ministry, He had little tolerance for those who considered themselves righteous, yet showed much mercy to those that the world would see as sinners. He expects his church to do the same today.

All things to all men

Paul's teachings from 1 Corinthians 8-10 show us much about how we Christians should be dealing with others. We don't insist on our rights nor demand that they behave like us; we mold our behavior to their needs. We don't participate in sin, but we don't place unnecessary burdens on others, either.

What does "becoming all things to all men" look like when dealing with...

...our non-Christian neighbors who practice things of which we don't approve

...new believers in Christ who aren't sure if they should practice things of which we approve

...long-time members who don't like things we are doing

...long-time members who feel they have the freedom to do things we don't think are correct

How do we let non-Christians see our beliefs without rejecting them for the things they do with which we aren't comfortable?

Prayerful participation

In this chapter, we looked at ten principles of prayerful participation

1. Get involved in your community.

Do you participate in non-church events that take place in your community?	Yes	No

What could you do to improve in this area?

2. Be aware of the people in your life.

Are you careful to take note of the people around you: fellow travelers on public transport, service people, coworkers, customers, cashiers?	Yes	No
What could you do to improve in this area?		

3. Meet your neighbors.

Are you actively trying to get to know people who live around you?	Yes	No
What could you do to improve in this area?		

4. Ask questions and listen to the answers.

Are you good at showing interest in other people?	Yes	No
What could you do to improve in this area?		

5. Remember that our neighbors need Jesus above all.

Do you find times and ways to insert Jesus into your conversations?	Yes	No

What could you do to improve in this area?		

6. Live Christ to earn the right to speak about Christ.

Does your life reflect your beliefs? Do others see you living for Christ?	Yes	No
What could you do to improve in this area?		

7. Remember who you are.

Are you confident in your identity as a Christian?	Yes	No
What could you do to improve in this area?		

8. Keep your eyes on the fruit of the Spirit.

Do your interactions with non-Christians lead to godly fruit, as listed in Galatians 5?	Yes	No
What could you do to improve in this area?		

9. Watch out for the works of the flesh.

Do your interactions with non-Christians lead to worldliness, as listed in Galatians 5?	Yes	No

What could you do to improve in this area?		

10. Pray.

Are you praying regularly about your relationships with outsiders?	Yes	No
What could you do to improve in this area?		

Work in progress

All too often, we expect a new convert to immediately be able to live like a mature Christian. That isn't how it works. In 1 Corinthians 8:7, Paul talks about new Christians who haven't yet fully understood that there is only one God; if he could accept such people as brothers, can't we show a little patience toward the new Christian who lets slip a foul word or two?

What are some areas with which new Christians frequently struggle?

What can we as a church do to correct new believers while still showing love? In other words, how do we show them they are doing something wrong without sounding like we are condemning them?

First John 1:7 tells us that the blood of Jesus will continually cleanse us if we are walking in the light. What does it mean to walk in the light? Does it mean to be perfect? Of course not; perfect people don't need cleansing.

Walking in the light has to do with seeking God, trying to do what He wants. When a believer stops trying, God stops removing his sin. The believer has chosen sin, and God respects that choice. But as long as we are trying to follow God, to walk in His path, He will cleanse us and make us right with Him.

The Christian is called to be holy in everything (1 Peter 1:15) and to be perfect as God is perfect (Matthew 5:48). Yet we know that God is ready and willing to forgive our sins when we seek His forgiveness. (1 John 1:9)

How do we teach new believers about God's forgiveness without making it sound like they have a license to sin?

How do we teach the need for holiness without teaching a works-based salvation?

CHAPTER 8

A LIFE LIKE LIGHTNING

Although the New Testament emphasizes that our salvation does not depend on works, and Jesus Himself warned against doing good deeds just to be seen by others, we still find a good number of passages that show us that what we do affects how others view us and our message. Look at these examples:

"You are the light of the world. A town built on a hill cannot be hidden. Neither do people light a lamp and put it under a bowl. Instead they put it on its stand, and it gives light to everyone in the house. In the same way, let your light shine before others, that they may see your good deeds and glorify your Father in heaven" (Matthew 5:14–17).

Jesus expected His followers to do good deeds in the sight of all so that everyone would praise God.

"You know what has happened throughout the province of Judea, beginning in Galilee after the baptism that John preached— how God anointed Jesus of Nazareth with the Holy Spirit and power, and how he went around doing good and healing all who were under the power of the devil, because God was with him" (Acts 10:37–38).

One of the hallmarks of the Jesus' ministry was that He went around doing good.

This service that you perform is not only supplying the needs of the Lord's people but is also overflowing in many expressions of thanks to God. Because of the service by which you have proved yourselves, others will praise God for the obedience that

> accompanies your confession of the gospel of Christ, and for your generosity in sharing with them and with everyone else (2 Corinthians 9:12–13).

The generosity of the Christians in giving to the needs of the poor resulted in people praising God.

> He must also have a good reputation with outsiders, so that he will not fall into disgrace and into the devil's trap. (1 Timothy 3:7)
>
> No widow may be put on the list of widows unless she is over sixty, has been faithful to her husband, and is well known for her good deeds, such as bringing up children, showing hospitality, washing the feet of the Lord's people, helping those in trouble and devoting herself to all kinds of good deeds (1 Timothy 5:9–10).

Both elders to lead the church and widows to be served by the church needed to be examples of good deeds.

> Who is wise and understanding among you? Let them show it by their good life, by deeds done in the humility that comes from wisdom (James 3:13).

James expects wise men to show their wisdom by doing good deeds.

> For it is God's will that by doing good you should silence the ignorant talk of foolish people (1 Peter 2:15).

Peter says that Christians can silence their critics by living lives dedicated to good works.

How do we live lives of public good deeds without falling into the hypocrisy Jesus mentions in Matthew 6?

Washing feet

In Jesus' day, footwashing had a meaning that it doesn't have today. It met an existing need (hygiene) and communicated a message (welcome). It was also an accepted cultural norm, practiced by religious and non-religious people alike.

What in our culture might be similar to footwashing?

How can Christians similarly communicate their love for one another in ways that fit our culture? Can you think of some creative acts of service? (some college students in one of my courses suggested providing valet parking for the elderly at church)

The church is called to serve the community around us, rather than try to control that community. We don't "lord over" non-Christians, but minister to them as Jesus reached out to a non-believing world.

How do we show those around us that we want to serve, not control?

What are some ways in which your church could "wash the feet" of the surrounding community?

Churches around the country and around the world are finding creative ways to serve the community around them. One church in Texas regularly purchases run-down houses in their small town, then refurbishes those homes and gives them away to deserving individuals.

One church in Tennessee has had Sundays where the offering plate is passed, and people are encouraged to take money out as they had need.

Many churches take one Sunday per month and spend their usual assembly time out in the community doing service projects.

Several churches have annual giveaway days, sort of like a huge garage sale except everything is free.

Congregations offer ESL classes and citizenship classes for foreigners. They have classes in basic business and finance principles to help individuals get on their feet. They babysit for moms, visit the sick, comfort the grieving, and serve their cities in countless ways. The only limit is your imagination!

Gifts in action

One of the keys to glorifying God through our deeds is making sure that we are doing our best to use the gifts God has given us.

Passages that talk about the different spiritual gifts that Christians have (like Romans 12:3-8; 1 Corinthians 12:4-31; 1 Peter 4:10-11) emphasize the fact that Christians receive different gifts to build up the body as a whole. We have to remember that:

- Different members have different gifts
- We don't choose our gifts; they are given to us as Jesus and the Spirit see fit.
- Gifts are not just for individual edification, but are for building up the body as a whole.
- The body needs all of the gifts that Jesus provides.
- The body can only grow when each part is doing its work.

As stated in chapter 4, there are three main stages to recognizing our gifts:

1. Prayer
2. Experimentation
3. Confirmation

Here's a checklist to think about when examining your gifts:

Have I studied the gifts mentioned in Romans 12, 1 Corinthians 12, Ephesians 4, and 1 Peter 4?	Yes	No

This is where you start. Recognize that some of the gifts mentioned are from the miraculous age in the early stages of the church. Keep in mind as well that these gifts are examples; they are not a complete list of every gift the Spirit may choose to give His church.

Have I spent sincere time in prayer, asking that God help me discover my gifts?	Yes	No

Gifts come from God; Who better to help us discover what our gifts are?

Have I worked in a variety of ministries in the church and in the community?	Yes	No

You will only be able to recognize your gifts as you use them. Open yourself up to a variety of ministry opportunities as you seek to find your gifts.

Do I especially enjoy doing certain ministries?	Yes	No
Are there good results when I perform certain ministries?	Yes	No
Do other Christians affirm me as I do certain ministry tasks?	Yes	No

We should expect to see a combination of these three things. Sometimes we like to do things at which we don't excel, but generally prayerful consideration of our gifts will help us find satisfaction in the things God has equipped us to do. And our gifts should build up the body and lead others to recognize the gifts we've received.

As we come to identify our gifts, we should also expect to find where and how to use those gifts. Our church leaders should be able to help us find ministry opportunities. As mentioned, we should also be open to God's calling, especially through "provocation of our spirit." We are often moved to notice needs in the church or in the community precisely because God is calling us to help meet those needs.

How well does your church match gifts to needs? Let's go through the checklist:

Leaders offer encouragement and support as members develop new ministries.				
Never	Rarely	Sometimes	Often	Always
Emphasis is on ministry that impacts the community outside the church building.				
Never	Rarely	Sometimes	Often	Always
Members are urged to meet needs rather than complain about them.				
Never	Rarely	Sometimes	Often	Always
Leaders are actively discovering new opportunities for ministry for members to be involved in.				
Never	Rarely	Sometimes	Often	Always
The church focuses its resources on ministries where members have gifts, rather than trying to do too many ministries.				
Never	Rarely	Sometimes	Often	Always
Members have the freedom to try new ministries and the freedom to allow existing ministries to cease.				
Never	Rarely	Sometimes	Often	Always

In which of these areas do you especially see a need for improvement?

PREPARING FOR HARVEST

Many of the original hearers of the material in the Bible were people who lived in agricultural settings. They knew well the cycles of sowing and reaping, cultivating the soil and bringing in the harvest. Because of that, the Bible often uses imagery taken from the fertile farmlands of Israel. Let's look at some of those passages:

> You transplanted a vine from Egypt; you drove out the nations and planted it. You cleared the ground for it, and it took root and filled the land (Psalms 80:8–9).
>
> The psalmist compares Israel to a vine that God Himself planted and cultivated.

> I will sing for the one I love a song about his vineyard: My loved one had a vineyard on a fertile hillside. He dug it up and cleared it of stones and planted it with the choicest vines. He built a watchtower in it and cut out a winepress as well. Then he looked for a crop of good grapes, but it yielded only bad fruit (Isaiah 5:1–2).
>
> According to Isaiah, God's people were a vineyard, one that had only produced bad fruit instead of good.

> He took one of the seedlings of the land and put it in fertile soil. He planted it like a willow by abundant water, and it sprouted and became a low, spreading vine. Its branches turned toward him, but its roots remained under it. So it became a vine and produced branches and put out leafy boughs (Ezekiel 17:5–6).

Like the other writers, Ezekiel compares the people of Israel to a plant that God planted and cared for.

The Parable of the Sower (Luke 8:4–15)

Jesus uses the imagery of seed falling on different types of soil to describe how people respond to the Word of God.

The Parable of the Sower II (Mark 4:26-29)

In another parable about sowing, Jesus uses the mysteries of plant growth to describe the growth of the kingdom of God.

"By their fruit you will recognize them. Do people pick grapes from thornbushes, or figs from thistles? Likewise every good tree bears good fruit, but a bad tree bears bad fruit. A good tree cannot bear bad fruit, and a bad tree cannot bear good fruit. Every tree that does not bear good fruit is cut down and thrown into the fire. Thus, by their fruit you will recognize them" (Matthew 7:16–20).

Just as plants will produce fruit according to their kind, so people produce fruit according to what is in their hearts.

The Parable of the Weeds Among the Wheat (Matthew 13:24–30)

By means of a story about weeds intentionally sown in a wheat field, Jesus reminds His listeners that not everyone who claims to be a follower of Jesus really is one. He also emphasizes that it is God who will ultimately separate the true followers from the false ones.

The Parable of the Fig Tree (Luke 13:6–9)

Jesus uses a story about a fig tree that didn't produce to illustrate God's patience and the limits of that patience.

> The Parable of the Mustard Seed (Luke 13:18-19)
>
> The tiny mustard seed illustrates the mysteries of the growth of God's kingdom.

> The Parable of the Wicked Tenants (Luke 20:9–16)
>
> Jesus reveals the wickedness of the Jewish rulers by telling a story of tenants of a vineyard who rebel against the landowner. This story prepares the Jews for the harsh consequences their rejection of Jesus would bring.

Why do you think the Bible so often uses agricultural imagery to reflect the way people respond to God?

Is this imagery as useful to modern readers as it was to people in Bible times? Is there another source of symbols that might communicate better today?

God makes things grow

Many of the parables drive home the point that it is God who makes things grow. Paul states this clearly in 1 Corinthians 3:6-7:

> I planted the seed, Apollos watered it, but God has been making it grow. So neither the one who plants nor the one who waters is anything, but only God, who makes things grow (1 Corinthians 3:6–7).

Why is it important to remember that only God can make things grow?

If only God makes things grow, does it matter what we do when reaching out to others? Why or why not?

Visualizing the journey

Let's look again at the discipleship process as presented in chapter 9:

STAGE	DESCRIPTION	OUR TASK
Uncultivated	Unaware of God, uninterested	Prayer
Cleared	Seeking spiritual answers	Presence
Plowed	Positive exposure to Christianity	Presenting God's Word
Sown	Challenged by the gospel	Proclaiming the gospel
Emergence = New birth!		
Visible growth	First steps as a Christian	Partnership
Harvest	Discipled and ready to disciple others	Perpetuating (passing it on)

In what ways does it help to visualize the road from unbelief to discipleship as a process?

How is spiritual growth comparable to agricultural growth? How is it different?

On a sheet of paper, draw a representation of your own spiritual journey. Include things like:

- Where did you begin? (**Christian home, complete ignorance of God, moral but unreligious family**)
- What were some of the milestones along your journey?
- Who were some of the people that were influential in your journey?
- Where do you feel you are right now compared to where you would like to be?

Decide on how you'd like to represent this process (**a road, a map, a plant, a building**).

God's fellow workers

One key element in outreach is the ability to be aware of those around us. If we're not careful, Christians can come to isolate ourselves from non-believers, focusing our emotional energy on those who already know God. We need to be conscious of the people in our lives who need to know more about God.

Start by making a list of names. At first, you may even have a few on your list whose names you don't know. Go ahead and write down "Guy at the convenience store," even if you don't know him by name.

Even if we may not know where people are in their relationship with God, we can know enough to guess how to help them in their journey. For now, we want to label as many of the names with one of the following labels: Prayer, Presence, Proclamation.

For some of the people on the list, the best we can do is pray. These are either the people we don't know well or the people we know are resistant to Christianity. Write "Prayer" next to their name.

There are others we know better and can see that they are open to knowing more about Christianity. With these people, we want to be sure that they are seeing what the church is doing in the community, as well as what you are doing. Remember, the goal isn't to make them fall in love with the church or praise you as a wonderful person. The goal is to attract them to God and His kingdom. You will write "Presence" next to their name.

Finally, there are some who are ready for proclamation. They are ready to talk about spiritual things. With this group, you can share Bible stories and Bible concepts. You can invite them to church activities where they will hear more about Jesus. You can begin to show them the gospel and how people respond to the gospel. "Proclamation" is what you write next to these names.

So your list will look something like this:

Don next door	Presence
Liz at the office	Prayer
Uncle Dave	Proclamation
Manager at Quik Burger	Prayer
David Jones (from soccer)	Presence

A SON OF SHALOM

When sending out his disciples in Luke 10:2-7, Jesus told them to look for "a son of peace" (Luke 10:6). Chapter 10 uses the term shalom, recognizing that this term includes more than just peace. We saw in chapter 6 that this term also refers to concepts like:

- health
- sound relationships
- prosperity
- success
- victory

These terms are not to be viewed separately; they are all aspects of what shalom is about. It's prosperity and success through sound relationships and peace. It's victory that brings peace, not a domination of others.

And shalom in the Bible comes from God, not from man's achievements.

The things listed in the definition of **shalom** seem to be things that almost everyone wants. What's the difference between someone who wishes for shalom and someone who is a child of **shalom**?

Why does such peace only come from God?

Chronos and kairos

This chapter talks about two other foreign words: **chronos** and **kairos**. *Chronos* refers to time in a quantitative sense: minutes, days, months, years. *Kairos* talks about time as being right or wrong; kairos is when it is the right time to do something.

> "Therefore Jesus told them, "My time is not yet here; for you any time will do" (John 7:6).

An important part of outreach is being able to discern the kairos, being able to spot the appropriate time to speak or act. More than spotting the precise moment when someone is ready to hear more about God, identifying the kairos is about recognizing the appropriate season in someone's life when he is open to learning.

One important thing to be aware of is special life events that make people more open to the gospel. This chapter mentions the following:

- Change in job situation, educational status, or location.
- Loss of significant individuals.
- Catastrophic events.
- Family transitions: marriage, divorce, parenthood.
- Holidays.

What are some other life events that might create an openness to the gospel?

Why do you think these moments in life tend to make people more aware of their need for God?

Making the most of the kairos

Be very careful, then, how you live—not as unwise but as wise, making the most of every opportunity (kairos), because the days are evil (Ephesians 5:15–16).

As we deal with people, we need to know how to make the most of the kairos that present themselves. We do this through the following:

▶ Hearing the *kairos*.
▶ Using non-threatening beginnings.
▶ Having *kairos* conversations.
▶ Spotting the child of shalom.

Let's flesh these out in a checklist:

When spending time with non-Christian friends, am I certain to listen more than I talk?	Yes	No

The old rule is that you listen twice as much as you talk; just remember, you have two ears and one mouth. We have to watch ourselves, because we are often anxious to share what we have learned. But we earn the right to speak by listening.

Am I manipulating the conversation or engaging in a shared dialogue?	Yes	No

Remember the findings mentioned in this chapter: When evangelists saw their job as transmitting information or using a preset set of questions and answers, those evangelists were far less effective. The most effective evangelists engaged in open dialogue with the people with whom they were talking.

Do I watch for life events that might make someone more open to hearing about God?	Yes	No

As seen in the section above, major life events (and minor events like holidays) often create openings for talking about God.

Do I know of non-threatening ways to reach out to someone who is open to learning more?	Yes	No

We need to be aware of what is available to us: DVDs or books we could loan them, websites we could share with them, projects in which we could include them, social events with other Christians, evangelistic Bible studies. As we involve ourselves in other people's lives and notice a spiritual awakening, we need to think about what sort of first step fits them best.

Am I comfortable with *kairos* conversations? Do I know what to say and not say?	Yes	No

Remember that a kairos conversation typically includes more questions than direct statements. Ask about their spiritual background. Learn about their personal history, their Bible knowledge, their understanding of God and basic points of Christianity. Watch for emotional responses that might warn you of sensitive areas. At the appropriate time, share your personal experience with the gospel. Remember your purposes: (1) determine their readiness; and (2) open the door to move the conversation to the next level.

Recognizing a child of shalom

At some point during these conversations, you should be able to recognize that the person is ready to understand the personal nature of the gospel and make a choice as to how to respond. Choose someone you know who might possibly be ready to talk about becoming a Christian. Answer these questions about that person.

Person's name:

Do you have a relationship of trust? Have you earned the right to talk to this person about spiritual things?

Do you know something about this person's spiritual background? Is there any religious "baggage" of which they need to rid themselves before becoming a Christian?

Do you know something about this person's personal background? Is there any personal "baggage" of which they need to rid themselves before becoming a Christian?

What needs have you discovered in this person's life? How can the gospel address those needs?

How much have you been able to share about your personal relationship with God?
Has the person been exposed to other members of your church?
What have you seen that shows the person to be receptive to the gospel?

If the person seems to be ready for a deeper conversation, now is the time to ask some important questions:

▶ Where are you in your spiritual journey?

▶ Are you ready to talk about taking the next step?

CHAPTER 11

GOOD NEWS
IS FOR SHARING

It was a full house in Capernaum. They were packed in, all eager to hear the things that Jesus had to say.

Four men came to the house, carrying their friend on a stretcher. I don't know how far they had to carry him, but I know that it took some effort to bring him to Jesus. Then when they got to the house, they couldn't get in.

So they took their friend up on the roof. Were there stairs? A ladder? We don't know. But if you've ever helped someone move into a second-floor apartment, you can imagine the difficulty they had in getting their friend up on the roof. Then they had to lower him down to where Jesus was.

That's a lot of trouble! Why would you do this? Simple...that's what you do for a friend. They believed that Jesus could heal their friend, and they were willing to do whatever it took to get him to Jesus (Mark 2:1-12).

Christians need the same attitude toward their friends. If we truly believe that Jesus has what our friends need, we should be willing to do whatever it takes to bring them to Jesus. At the appropriate time, that includes telling them how to become a Christian.

What sort of things get in our way as we think about bringing people to Jesus?

Defining the gospel

It's always enlightening to look at what the New Testament talks about as "gospel." Though some would limit this to what's found in 1 Corinthians 15 (death, burial, resurrection of Jesus), a look at more passages gives us a broader view of the good news.

The beginning of the good news about Jesus the Messiah, the Son of God (Mark 1:1).

It never hurts to remember that the whole story of Jesus is good news: His life, His ministry, His death, His resurrection, His reign in heaven, His second coming.

And with many other words John exhorted the people and proclaimed the good news to them (Luke 3:18).

John preached the gospel before people even met Jesus. What was this good news? God was forgiving sins and sending the Chosen One.

Jesus went throughout Galilee, teaching in their synagogues, proclaiming the good news of the kingdom, and healing every disease and sickness among the people (Matthew 4:23).

After John was put in prison, Jesus went into Galilee, proclaiming the good news of God. "The time has come," he said. "The kingdom of God has come near. Repent and believe the good news!" (Mark 1:14–15)

But he said, "I must preach the good news of the kingdom of God to the other towns also, because that is why I was sent" (Luke 4:43).

The good news of the kingdom was...the kingdom is near! God's kingdom was breaking into this world, and that was good news indeed.

Day after day, in the temple courts and from house to house, they never stopped teaching and proclaiming the good news that Jesus is the Messiah (Acts 5:42).

The fact that Jesus is God's Messiah is the gospel that the early church preached.

Now, brothers and sisters, I want to remind you of the gospel I preached to you, which you received and on which you have taken your stand. By this gospel you are saved, if you hold firmly to the word I preached to you. Otherwise, you have believed in vain. For what I received I passed on to you as of first importance: that Christ died for our sins according to the Scriptures, that he was buried, that he was raised on the third day according to the Scriptures, and that he appeared to Cephas [Peter], and then to the Twelve (1 Corinthians 15:1–5).

Though it's a mistake to consider this passage as a telling of the whole gospel, it certainly reflects what is at the heart of the good news: the sacrifice of Jesus.

Remember Jesus Christ, raised from the dead, descended from David. This is my gospel... (2 Timothy 2:8)

Jesus, fulfilling prophecy through His birth and through His death, is the gospel.

Reading through these passages, how would you summarize the gospel that's presented in the New Testament?

Here are the points that were presented in this chapter, most of which come from the above passages:

- Jesus is the Eternal Word who was with God in the beginning, who is God, and became flesh.
- Jesus is the fulfillment of the great promises of the Old Testament. Through Jesus, we become part of God's chosen people, spiritual descendants of Abraham.

- Jesus came to bring God's kingdom to this world.
- Jesus lived a sinless life despite being tempted in every way as we are.
- Jesus died on a cross because of our sin.
- Jesus was buried in a tomb and came back to life on the third day.
- Jesus will come again to judge the living and the dead.

What would you add to this list?

Obeying the gospel

The New Testament speaks of obeying the gospel (2 Thessalonians 1:8). There is a natural response to this good news. In the Old Testament, God expected His people to respond to His love by being faithful to Him and His Law. The new covenant has similar expectations.

From the Acts 2 presentation in this chapter, we see the following response points:
- Believe the facts about Jesus.
- Recognize him as Lord and Savior.
- Admit your sin, your need for salvation.
- Repent.
- Be baptized.
- Become an active part of the Lord's church.

What would you add to this list, either from Acts 2 or other passages?

Presenting the gospel

However we choose to go about it, when we present the gospel, we need to present two main things:

1. Jesus.
2. How to respond to Jesus.

There are different methods available. Based on the concepts we saw in the previous chapter, I would encourage you to steer away from the manipulative dialogues that have often been taught. You need something that can be presented in a conversational style, as part of an open dialogue.

In your own words, describe how you would go about presenting the gospel to someone else.

The priority of the gospel

Back in that packed house in Capernaum, Jesus watched as four men lowered their friend down from the roof. He saw the care they took. He knew the effort they'd put into getting their friend to Jesus' feet. He recognized faith, faith that believes in the power of the Son of God.

So He looked at this paralyzed man and said, "Your sins are forgiven."

If I were one of the four on the roof, I wouldn't be happy. Not at all. I hadn't gone to all that trouble so that this rabbi could speak words of religious comfort. I wanted my friend to walk!

If I were the man on the mat, I'd be perfectly content. For Jesus had taken care of my greatest need.

Jesus looks at the world and sees cripples everywhere. People crippled by sin and handicapped by the weakness of their flesh, their inability to resist temptation. And He offers what this world needs most: forgiveness of sins.

Christians look at the world and see physical needs. We go to great length to clothe and house and feed and heal. Those are good things. Those are great things! This is holy service.

But if we don't share Jesus with people, we haven't really helped them. If they don't receive forgiveness of sins, their greatest needs have gone untouched.

How do we balance our desire to meet physical needs with the necessity of attending to spiritual needs? How do we minister to body and soul, tending to one while not neglecting the other?

How do we refocus our mission trips so that the mission doesn't get lost along the way? What can we do to ensure that the gospel is presented alongside every good deed that is done?

CHAPTER 12

CITIZENS OF THE KINGDOM

When someone moves to a new country, he often spends time studying about his new home before going there. He often spends time learning the language and some of the customs before launching into a normal routine. Those who don't, often experience severe culture shock.

As new Christians become a part of the church community, they need a similar time of learning. It's up to those of us who have been Christians for years to step up and help the new members find their way around.

Passing the torch

Throughout the Bible, we are reminded of the importance of passing information from one generation to another. Consider these passages:

On that day tell your son, 'I do this because of what the LORD did for me when I came out of Egypt' (Exodus 13:8).

Several times in the Law, God talks about using the Passover and other feasts as teaching moments for future generations.

Fix these words of mine in your hearts and minds; tie them as symbols on your hands and bind them on your foreheads. Teach them to your children, talking about them when you sit at home and when you walk along the road, when you lie down and when you get up (Deuteronomy 11:18–19).

Younger generations were to be taught God's command-ments. They couldn't just give them a book; books weren't that common. The laws had to be passed down from generation to generation.

Each of you is to take up a stone on his shoulder, according to the number of the tribes of the Israelites, to serve as a sign among you. In the future, when your children ask you, 'What do these stones mean?' tell them that the flow of the Jordan was cut off before the ark of the covenant of the LORD (Joshua 4:5–7).

God had His people set up a memorial so that they could teach their children and grandchildren about how God brought them into the land of Canaan.

He decreed statutes for Jacob and established the law in Israel, which he commanded our ancestors to teach their children, so the next generation would know them, even the children yet to be born, and they in turn would tell their children (Psalms 78:5–6).

The Israelites were to teach the law from generation to generation, even thinking about those who hadn't been born yet.

Tell it to your children, and let your children tell it to their children, and their children to the next generation (Joel 1:3).

A great calamity had come upon Israel because of their unfaithfulness, and the prophet wanted to be sure future generations knew what had happened and why.

And the things you have heard me say in the presence of many witnesses entrust to reliable people who will also be qualified to teach others (2 Timothy 2:2).

The church used this same system to pass things on from Christian to Christian, from one faith generation to the next.

Just as families were to pass down information, so Christians are to be sure that those younger in faith come to know what they have learned.

Did someone make sure that you were taught when you became a Christian? If so, how did they go about it?

What does your congregation do to make sure that young Christians receive the care and training they need?

Imitating Christ

We sometimes talk about wanting to imitate the first-century church. I don't think that's a good idea. If we look at the first-century church, it was full of problems, from the divisions and drunkenness in Corinth to the embracing of false teaching in Galatia. The early church was a human bunch.

Recently on the radio, I heard a car expert giving advice to someone who was having trouble with the ignition of his car. The expert told the person to get a new key made. He told him, however, to go to the dealer to get the new key. Other shops would merely make a copy from the key the person already had; the dealer could make a key that would precisely fit the ignition.

Rather than copying a copy, we should copy the original: Jesus. We don't make imitating early Christians our goal; our goal is to imitate Jesus Christ.

Think about these passages:

> "The student is not above the teacher, but everyone who is fully trained will be like their teacher" (Luke 6:40).

> Follow my example, as I follow the example of Christ (1 Corinthians 11:1).

> For those God foreknew he also predestined to be conformed to the image of his Son, that he might be the firstborn among many brothers and sisters (Romans 8:29).

> And we all, who with unveiled faces contemplate the Lord's glory, are being transformed into his image with ever-increasing glory, which comes from the Lord, who is the Spirit (2 Corinthians 3:18).

> Instead, speaking the truth in love, we will grow to become in every respect the mature body of him who is the head, that is, Christ (Ephesians 4:15).

> Let us fix our eyes on Jesus, the pioneer and perfecter of faith. For the joy set before him he endured the cross, scorning its shame, and sat down at the right hand of the throne of God (Hebrews 12:2).

There have been times when some have wanted to de-emphasize the gospels, claiming they don't address the needs of the New Testament church. This is a serious misunderstanding of what the gospels are. They are documents prepared by the church, for the church, so that people would know how Jesus lived and what He taught. If we are going to imitate Christ, studying the gospels should be a priority for us.

In this life, Christians will never be as perfect as Jesus was nor as holy as God is. Yet by striving after those goals, we will be better followers than we would be otherwise.

Do churches place the proper emphasis on the imitation of Christ? Explain your answer.

Do the gospels have the place of prominence they should have in our Bible study? How can we focus more on what Jesus said and did?

The basics of faith

From Acts 2:42, we learn some of the basic building blocks of the spiritual life:

1. Bible study   3. Breaking bread

2. Fellowship   4. Prayer

Let's think about some of the basic things we need to teach young Christians about each of these. What sort of things would you teach them about each of these areas?

Bible study	Navigation - How do we find our way around in the Bible?
	Interpretation - How do we read and understand the Bible?

	Application - How do we live out the things that we study?
Fellowship	Sharing time - The importance of being together
	Sharing goods - The importance of helping one another
	Sharing burdens - The importance of carrying each other's loads
Breaking Bread	Lord's Supper - Meaning of the weekly meal

	Potlucks - Meaning of fellowship meals
	Daily bread - Meaning of our daily meals
Prayer	How to pray
	When to pray
	What to pray

CHAPTER 13

BEING THE CHURCH, INSIDE AND OUT

Let's examine the analogy of the long lost Shakespearean play. If you were in the theater company that was trying to put on the play, how would you determine the following?

- How the story should proceed

- What tone the play should have (drama, comedy, romance)

- What each character should say

- Where each scene should take place

What other things would you need to consider?

Too often, we read the Bible looking only for commands that we can quote to one another. We don't always know how to deal with stories, and stories make up a huge part of the Bible.

How does the analogy of the lost play give us insight into how we can learn from the stories we find in the Bible?

Inward, upward, outward

The body of Christ needs to grow inward, upward, and outward. We grow together as a body, we grow closer to God, and we grow by reaching out to others.

What do we expect to see as signs of inward growth?

What do we expect to see as signs of upward growth?

What do we expect to see as signs of outward growth?

In which of these areas is your church the strongest?

In which of these areas does your church most need to improve?

In which of these areas are you the strongest?

In which of these areas do you most need to improve?

Stewards of God's time

We are stewards of God's time. He entrusts us with a certain amount, and we are to administer it as best we can. We are to make sure that God is at the center of every hour of our day.

How are you doing at glorifying God in your daily life?

I always do my best, working for God, not just for my boss (teacher).				
Never	Rarely	Sometimes	Often	Always
In my daily life, I try to reflect the nature of God (truth, love, justice)				
Never	Rarely	Sometimes	Often	Always
I make an effort to improve the day of everyone with whom I have contact.				
Never	Rarely	Sometimes	Often	Always
I'm willing to bring prayer into my daily interactions with others.				
Never	Rarely	Sometimes	Often	Always
As best I can, I try to watch for those around me who are seeking God.				
Never	Rarely	Sometimes	Often	Always

What are two things that you could do that would help you do better at using each day for God?

Meanwhile back in the sheep pen

The church grows as each part does its work. That means that each member is encouraged to find his gift and use it. When we come together in our assemblies, we each bring a unique offering of realized gifts. That's the beauty of a body!

How can the church help members value their own gifts, rather than envying the gifts others have received?

How can the church better recognize and celebrate a wide variety of gifts, not just the ones that are typically on display during a church service?

What can we do to be sure that our gifts are being used for the good of the whole body, not just the good of a few?

How do we encourage those sitting in the pews to use their gifts when we come together, even if they aren't the ones up front leading?

Fruit inspectors

> The acts of the flesh are obvious: sexual immorality, impurity and debauchery; idolatry and witchcraft; hatred, discord, jealousy, fits of rage, selfish ambition, dissensions, factions and envy; drunkenness, orgies, and the like. I warn you, as I did before, that those who live like this will not inherit the kingdom of God. But the fruit of the Spirit is love, joy, peace, patience, kindness, goodness, faithfulness, gentleness and self-control. Against such things there is no law (Galatians 5:19–23).

As you use your gifts and carry out your ministry, what are you seeing? Fruit of the spirit or works of the flesh?

Which works of the flesh are the most troublesome to you in your work with the church? That is, which ones try to show up in you and in your ministry?

Which aspect of the fruit of the Spirit is most elusive for you? What could you do to better cultivate that aspect?

Beyond our wildest dreams

> Now to him who is able to do immeasurably more than all we ask or imagine, according to his power that is at work within us, to him be glory in the church and in Christ Jesus throughout all generations, for ever and ever! Amen (Ephesians 3:20–21).

It's time to dream! Write below what you would like your church to look like five years from now: